ELECTRONICS
RESOURCES

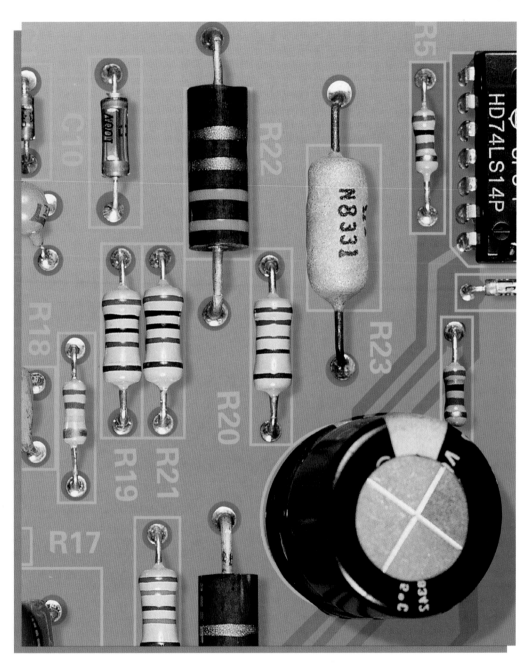

DEVELOPED AT LAWRENCE HALL OF SCIENCE, UNIVERSITY OF CALIFORNIA AT BERKELEY
PUBLISHED AND DISTRIBUTED BY DELTA EDUCATION

FOSS MIDDLE SCHOOL PROJECT STAFF AND ASSOCIATES

FOSS Middle School Curriculum Development Team
Dr. Lawrence F. Lowery, Principal Investigator
Linda De Lucchi, Co-Director
Larry Malone, Co-Director
Anthony Cody, Curriculum Developer
Ted Stoeckley, Curriculum Developer
Dr. Susan Brady, Curriculum Developer
Susan Kaschner Jagoda, Curriculum Developer
Dr. Kathy Long, Assessment Coordinator
Cheryl Webb, Program Assistant
Carol Sevilla, Graphic Designer
Rose Craig, Artist
Mark Warren, Equipment Manager

Electronics Multimedia Design Team
Dr. Marco Molinaro, Director
Dr. Susan Ketchner, Producer
Dr. Robert Guralnick, Revisions Producer
Rebecca Shapley, Revisions Producer
Leigh Anne McConnaughey, Principal Illustrator
Wolf Read, Senior Illustrator
Sue Whitmore, Senior Illustrator
Amy Todd, Illustrator
Richard Blair, Head Programmer on original version
Tom McTavish, Head Programmer on 2001 version
Dan Bluestein, Programmer on 2001 version
Richard Hyde, Systems Administrator
Guillaume Brasseur, Computer Administrator and QA Manager
Alicia Nieves, Quality Assurance
Loretta Hintz, Video Editor
Avery Kramer, A/V specialist

Special Contributors and Consultants
Dr. Lawrence D. Woolf, Applied Physics, General Atomics, Content Advisor and Curriculum Reviewer
Matthew Gilliland, Electrical Engineer, Content Advisor
Marshall Montgomery, Materials Design
Alan Gould, Lawrence Hall of Science, Content Advisor for Multimedia
Rockman ET AL., Evaluators

Delta Education FOSS Middle School Team
Mathew Bacon, Jeanette Wall, Bonnie Piotrowski, Tom Guetling, Dave Vissoe, Grant Gardner
John Prescott, Joann Hoy, Cathrine Monson

National Trial Teachers
Scott Seidler, Booth-Fickett Magnet School, Tucson, AZ; **Evelyn Rayford,** North Heights Junior High School, Texarkana, AR
Pris Brutlag, Parsons Middle School, Redding, CA; **Lorraine Usher,** Borel Middle School, San Mateo, CA
Kathy Ludlam, Mt. Garfield Middle School, Clifton, CO; **Ginger Willms,** West Middle School, Grand Junction, CO
Sheree Vessels, Southern Oaks Middle School, Port St. Lucie, FL; **Lisa Evans,** Southern Oaks Middle School, Port St. Lucie, FL
Linda Rose, Derby Middle School, Derby, KS; **Linda Murtagh,** JFK Middle School, Hudson, MA
Jeffrey Schroeder, Pine Island Public School, Pine Island, MN; **Craig Erickson,** Pine Island Public School, Pine Island, MN
John Kuzma, McManus Middle School, Linden, NJ; **Gayle Dunlap,** Walter T. Bergen Middle School, Bloomingdale, NJ
Donna Moran, Walter T. Bergen Middle School, Bloomingdale, NJ; **Nicole Kennedy,** Middle School #324, Brooklyn, NY
Dr. Jodi Haney, Bowling Green State University, Bowling Green, OH; **Teri Dannenberg,** Memorial Preparatory Schools, Garland, TX
Scott Stier, Badger Middle School, West Bend, WI; **Doug Zarling,** Badger Middle School, West Bend, WI

Lawrence Hall of Science

FOSS for Middle School Project
Lawrence Hall of Science, University of California
Berkeley, CA 94720 510-642-8941

...*because children learn by doing.*®

Delta Education
P.O. Box 3000 80 Northwest Blvd.
Nashua, NH 03063 1-800-258-1302

The FOSS Middle School Program was developed in part with the support of the National Science Foundation Grant ESI 9553600. However, any opinions, findings, conclusions, statements, and recommendations expressed herein are those of the authors and do not necessarily reflect the views of the NSF.

Electronics
4 5 6 7 8 9 10 QUE 09 08 07 06 05

542-1415
1-58356-420-9

FOSS ELECTRONICS
RESOURCES

TABLE OF CONTENTS

WHAT'S IN A LAMP?

You've undoubtedly noticed that cartoon characters always sport a lightbulb over their heads when they are suddenly struck with an idea. It makes sense. A lightbulb is bright, and it throws light on the subject. That's a nice symbol for a brilliant idea.

Lightbulbs are examples of lamps. A lamp is simply a source of light. Before the development of electricity, lamps burned oil to produce light. A cloth wick was placed in a container of light oil and lit on fire. Because the oil burned at a lower temperature than the wick, the oil burned off the wick without burning the wick itself. The lamp burned until the oil was all used up.

The same is true for electric lamps, in a way: they burn until the supply of electricity is used up. We know that, unlike the cartoon idea lamps, real electric lamps don't start shining all by themselves. They need electricity. By running electric current through the lamp, light shines forth. But how does the lamp produce light?

For electricity to flow through the lamp, there has to be a complete pathway made of conductors, called a circuit. Look at the

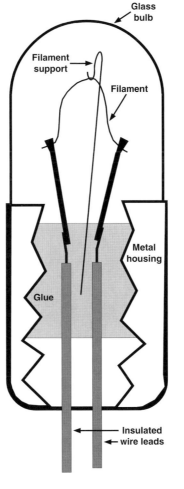

Glass bulb

Filament support

Filament

Metal housing

Glue

Insulated wire leads

cutaway picture and follow the path. An insulated copper wire enters the bottom of the lamp. Connected to this is a metal support wire that is clamped onto one end of a thin structure called the **filament.** The other end of the filament is clamped in a second metal support, which connects to the other wire that passes out of the lamp. That's the pathway, but it still doesn't explain the light.

When the lamp is connected to a battery (or other source of electricity), current flows through the circuit, including the filament. When the current "crowds through" the thin filament, the energy in the electricity heats it up. If a material gets hot enough, it gives off light. We know that when something is red hot, it is really hot. It looks red because it is giving off red light. If it gets hotter, it eventually gets white hot. That is what a modern electric lamp is—a material heated to such a high temperature that it gives off white light. This is an **incandescent** lamp.

The concept is simple compared to the problem of finding a material that can give off white heat without literally burning up. One of the people who took on the problem, and who is usually credited with developing a workable electric lamp, was Thomas Edison. In his Menlo Park, New Jersey, laboratory, he and his colleagues made thousands of materials into filaments and ran electricity through them. All the filaments went up in flames after one short burst of white light.

A major breakthrough came with the idea of sealing the filament inside a glass bulb from which the air had been removed. The idea was that, if no oxygen were around the filament, it would not burn up. The idea was successful, and in 1878, Edison produced an incandescent lamp with a carbon filament that burned for hours.

Since Edison's day the lamp has been improved in countless ways. In 1911 the tungsten filament was developed, and it is still used today. Hydrofluoric acid was used to etch the inner surface of the glass globe to diffuse the light, producing a softer glow. Today inert gases fill the glass bulbs, replacing air.

OTHER LAMPS

Not every lamp has a filament. Amusement parks and city centers are great places to look for other kinds of lamps. Discharge tubes are gas-filled glass cylinders that have electric contacts at each end. Those long glass tubes, bent into letters, faces, and other familiar shapes, are neon lights. When electricity flows through a tube filled with the gas neon, it emits bright red light. When other gases are used in place of neon, other colors result. Clever bending of tubes can result in a fantastic display of artistic lighting.

Another kind of discharge tube is used extensively for indoor lighting, especially in places like office buildings, hospitals, and schools. These fluorescent lamps are filled with mercury vapor, which emits ultraviolet light when electricity flows through it. UV light is invisible to humans. But, when UV light strikes a phosphor coating inside the tube, the excited phosphor coating emits a bright white light. The process is called fluorescence. Even though this process seems a little complicated, it is popular where lots of lighting is required, because fluorescent lamps use a lot less electricity to produce the light.

Why is fluorescent lighting more cost effective? Making light from electricity requires energy transformation. Incandescent lamps produce light by heating a filament to an extremely high temperature. Most of the energy is transformed into heat, which is a by-product of the light-producing process. Fluorescent lighting, on the other hand, generates far less heat, so less energy is transformed into an undesirable by-product. Less waste, more efficiency.

The most efficient lighting systems use yet another technology to produce light. This lighting breakthrough will be discussed later in this course.

COMPONENT SYMBOLS AND SCHEMATICS

art of being a responsible scientist or engineer is keeping complete and accurate records of experiments and discoveries. Good records allow the engineer to look back at earlier work to recall details, and they are excellent tools for communication with others.

Electrical engineers and circuit designers make records of their circuits using **symbols** to represent the components, and standardized drawings called **schematic diagrams,** or simply **schematics,** to show how they connect components.

The symbols used to represent components are in some cases grossly simplified drawings of the component themselves. The symbol for a lamp can be seen as a filament inside a glass bulb. The switch symbol looks a bit like an old-fashioned knife switch, and simple lines are similar to wires.

The symbol for an electric cell reaches back to a time when two metal plates were immersed in a chemical bath to create a voltaic cell. The two lines, one shorter than the other, represent the two metal plates. By convention, the shorter plate is the negative terminal of the cell. (Remember, the shorter line is minus a little bit of its length.) A battery is nothing more nor less than two or more cells hooked together to make a battery of cells. In schematic drawings the symbol for a cell is often used to represent a battery, with the voltage of the battery written by the symbol.

The resistor symbol is interesting. Historically, a long, thin wire was used to put resistance into a circuit. To save space, the long wire was wrapped into a coil. If you visualize the resistor symbol as a coil, rather like a spring, viewed from the side, it resembles the zigzag resistor symbol.

Wire

Battery

Switch

Lamp

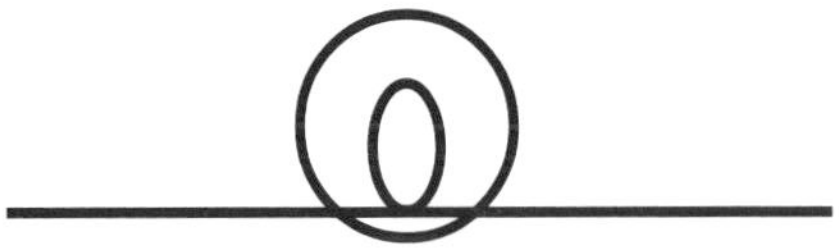

Resistor

Diode

LED

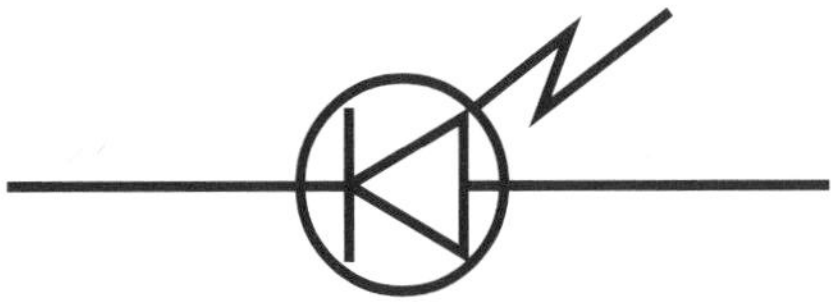

Capacitor

In schematics the lines representing conductive pathways are always laid out with square corners to make the diagrams nice and neat. Compare the drawing of a circuit on a spring board and the schematic drawing below it. Do they represent the same circuit?

As you can see, reality can be messy. That's where schematics become very useful. When the circuit is reduced to clean, geometric connections, the concept of the circuit design is much easier to understand.

About Current...

When scientists first discovered the flow of electric current, they thought that positive charge flowed from the positive battery terminal to the negative terminal. This is called **conventional current.** This is the model for current flow used by electrical engineers. In this course conventional current, flowing from positive to negative, is used most of the time.

Many years later the electron was discovered. Research showed that the negatively charged electron was the unit of charge that flowed through circuits. A second explanation of current, called **electron flow,** describes current starting at the negative battery terminal and flowing to the positive terminal. Electron flow is scientifically more accurate, but the conventional current model is still the most widely used way to describe current in circuits.

This course uses conventional current—plus to minus— except when detailed explanations of how components work are discussed. In these cases it is useful to try to understand what electrons are doing when components do their work. In these cases it will be clearly pointed out that the electron flow model of current is being used.

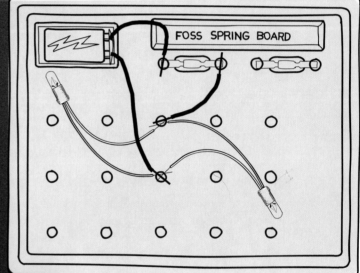

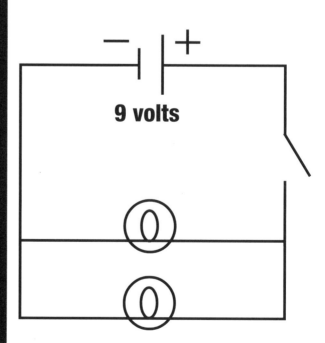

9 volts

decoding resistors

Resistors are conductors of electric current. What separates them from other conductors is that resistors don't conduct as well as, say, a copper wire. In fact, some resistors are such poor conductors that only a tiny bit of current can squeeze through. Resistors resist the flow of electric current.

The amount of resistance imposed by a resistor can vary widely. The unit of resistance is the ohm (Ω). A resistor with 2 or 3 Ω of resistance doesn't reduce the current much at all, but resistors that impose thousands or even millions of ohms have a significant effect on the current.

Resistors come in all different ohm ratings. We can refer to them as big resistors, and small resistors, but keep in mind that *big* and *small* don't refer to the *size* of the resistor, but to the *amount of resistance* it imposes on the current.

Electrical engineers need to know how many ohms a resistor will place in a circuit, so every resistor has its value written on it. Because resistors are so small, there isn't room to write a number, particularly a large number like 100,000 Ω. Instead, the value is written in a color code.

Typically a resistor will have four color bands painted around it like four colorful bracelets. One band appears by itself at one end of the resistor. A gold band informs the user that the resistor is guaranteed to be no more than 5% above or below the value at which the resistor is rated. That is, if the resistor is rated at 100 Ω, the gold band guarantees it to be between 95 Ω and 105 Ω. A silver band guarantees no more than 10% variance from the rated value.

The three color bands at the other end tell the value of the resistor in ohms. Each color represents a number. Here is the code.

black	= 0		green	= 5
brown	= 1		blue	= 6
red	= 2		violet	= 7
orange	= 3		gray	= 8
yellow	= 4		white	= 9

Here's how to decode the color bands.

1. The color band at the end is decoded as a number, using the code above.

2. The middle color band is also decoded as a number.

3. The third band tells you how many zeroes to write after the first two numbers.

Here is an example.

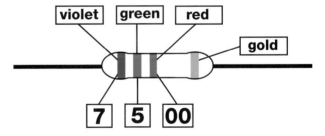

The third band is the tricky one. Until you have decoded several resistors, you might forget and just write the number of the color band instead of that number of zeroes.

How will you ever remember the code? You might memorize the order (after black and brown are the colors of the rainbow, then gray and white); or make up a little saying, called a mnemonic; or best of all, get out colored pencils and make a little reference card to keep handy in your notebook.

Did you ever try to wash a cat or run into a really strong wind? If so, you undoubtedly encountered some resistance. **Resistance** is any force working against an action you are trying to accomplish. Resistance is opposition. Airplanes have to overcome air resistance when they fly; fish work against water resistance when they swim; nails have to be driven with a hammer to penetrate the resistance imposed by wood; and, yes, a cat will resist your efforts to give it a bath.

Electricity moving through a complete circuit (a pathway of conductors) is called **current.** Current flows quite easily through some materials, like copper wires and silver rings. On the other hand, current doesn't flow at all through materials like glass, plastic, and wood. Good conductors impose little resistance to the flow of current; insulators impose a lot of resistance to the flow of current.

Carbon is an element. Carbon can be processed in a number of ways to make it conduct current. Depending how it is processed, carbon can be a very good conductor or a downright poor conductor. Because of this flexibility, carbon can be made into resistors with just about any amount of resistance. The resistors used in this electronics course are carbon resistors.

To get an idea about how carbon resistors do their job, we should start by considering how conductors promote the flow of current. If we looked deep into a piece of copper, we would see that it is made of copper atoms. Each atom has a nucleus, around which is buzzing a family of 29 electrons, like planets around a star, but these little planets don't have predictable orbits. The tiny electrons are the

key to conductivity.

Electrons are negatively charged. Each electron has exactly the same negative charge. Electrons are associated with their atomic nucleus, but some of them, those farthest from the nucleus, are free to move around. These loosely associated electrons are called free electrons. Free electrons can move from nucleus to nucleus if there is some force urging them to do so.

A battery is like an electron pump. When it is sitting on the shelf, it is charged up and ready to pump as soon as it is provided an opportunity to do so. When it is hooked up to a complete circuit made of conductors, it starts pushing electrons out of the negative terminal. The electrons pushed into the copper wire start a process like a line of dominos extending across a table. When you push over the first one, it pushes over the second one, and so on

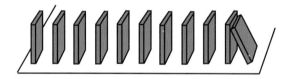

until the last one falls off the edge of the table. Notice, the domino that made the first push is

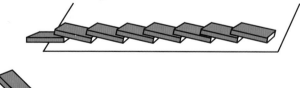

not the one that fell off the table. It looks like a domino went clear across the table, but it was just the push that went clear across the table.

So that's a model for what happens in the copper with the electrons. One electron gets bumped away from its nucleus, flies into space until it encounters another copper atom, and bumps another electron out to fly off. That's how electron current flows through a conductor—free electrons driven from atom to atom as they move through the wire.

Glass has no free electrons; the electrons orbiting the atoms in glass are dedicated to their nuclei. Therefore, no electrons get bumped, and no current flows. But, if you have a material that has *some* free electrons, *some* current will flow. And if you add to the material some atoms that actually interfere with the movement of electrons, you have a resistive material and you can make a resistor.

SCATTERING CENTERS

The atoms that interfere with the flow of electrons are called **scattering centers.** A scattering center is like a traffic diverter in a road.

Imagine there is a rock concert in the next city. You need to drive south out of town to the freeway, get on, and then motor over to the stadium. Sounds great. Trouble is, the city installed traffic diverters on all the roads leading south out of town. When you come to a diverter, you have to turn to the right or left. The traffic diverter (scattering center) makes you turn in a direction you didn't want to go. If the same thing is happening on all the other roads heading south, traffic will be zigzagging all over the place instead of proceeding smoothly south.

Eventually you will reach your destination, but you had to travel much farther and longer than it would take without the traffic diverters. The net effect is that the number of cars making it to the freeway each minute is far fewer than it would be without traffic diverters sending cars all over town.

The traffic diverters are the scattering centers that impose a force in opposition to the progress you intend to make toward the freeway. The city full of diverters is a resistor, and it reduces the flow of traffic making it to the freeway each minute. A graphic of the effect of scattering-center concentration in a conductor might look like this.

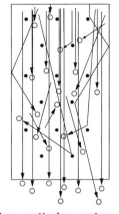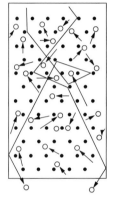

Few scattering centers: low resistance **Many scattering centers: high resistance**

• = scattering center
○ = electron
→ = direction of electron after collision

Once on the freeway, you can step on it and try to get to the concert on time, and, when you look around, you note that there are a lot fewer cars than there would have been if cars got smoothly onto the freeway. The number of cars per minute going past any point on the freeway is the same as the number of cars making it *to* the freeway each minute. The current, or flow of cars, is the same throughout the system because the resistor reduced the current of cars back in the city.

Some people like to think of resistance as potholes in the road, making cars slow down and dodge around, thus reducing the flow. Others make sense out of resistance by thinking of a five-lane road constricting to one or two lanes because of roadwork. These models get at the basic idea of resistance, too.

POTENTIOMETERS

The potentiometer is a resistor that you can control with the twist of a knob. The volume control on your television is a potentiometer. How does that work?

It involves a variable that determines the amount of resistance an object will impose in a circuit. Let's see if we can figure out what that variable is. Here is a diagram of a potentiometer that can vary from 0 Ω to 1000 Ω. Illustration A shows it set for 0 Ω; illustration B shows it set for 1000 Ω. What's the difference?

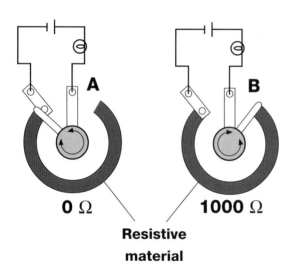

Resistive material

In illustration A none of the resistive material is included in the circuit. The current enters the potentiometer at the contact near the letter A and goes right back to the battery without passing through any of the resistive material. Consequently, the potentiometer imposes no

resistance in the circuit. Will the lamp be dim or bright?

In illustration B the current enters near the letter B, and in order to return to the battery, it must travel through the whole length of the resistive material. The potentiometer in this case is set to 1000 Ω. And how will the lamp look?

You can imagine the amount of resistance the potentiometer will impose when the knob is turned halfway between A and B—about 500 Ω. The farther a current travels through a resistive material, the greater the resistance.

Engineers who design carbon resistors know how to mix the carbon medium to get just the right concentration of scattering centers, and how far apart to position the contacts in the medium to produce resistors with values from a fraction of an ohm to millions of ohms—a resistor for every occasion.

THINK QUESTIONS

1. Think of another analogy for scattering centers—something that adds resistance to a system.

2. If you wanted to make a potentiometer that ranged from 0 Ω to 2000 Ω, how might you do that?

3. Resistors reduce the energy in a circuit. What do you think happens to the "lost" energy?

THE THREE GREAT TRUTHS OF CIRCUITRY

Before we get down to the truths, let's start off with a fiction. It's lunch time on a nice day, and you are having lunch outside. Your friend digs a soda out of her lunch bag and sets it on the table. Directly overhead, on the second floor of the school building, your science teacher also takes out a soda and sets it on the sill of the window. If either your friend or your science teacher were to be a little careless, a soda might be knocked so that it fell on your foot. Which can of soda would you rather have fall on your foot?

Pretty silly question. The real question is why would it be so much worse to get hit by the second-story soda than the tabletop soda? The answer is the potential energy in the second-story soda has the ability to do a lot more work than the tabletop soda. The difference between the amount of work that the high and low sodas can do is significant. And the work you intuitively know the sodas can do is compress your toe in a most painful manner.

Potential is also a key concept in electric circuitry. The potential in electric systems is the potential to push electrons through conductors. The potential in the batteries you use in class is 9 volts (V). The potential in the wall socket is about 120 V, and the potential in a bolt of lightning might be as high as 1,000,000 V! Voltage is the push that moves electrons through conductors.

If you put a voltmeter across the terminals of a 9-V battery, it will measure the difference in potential between them. You can visualize one terminal as being on the second floor, and the other on the table. The difference in potential between the "height" of the two terminals is the amount of work the battery can do.

VOLTAGE DROP

When a conductive pathway, like a little incandescent lamp, connects the two terminals of a 9-V battery, current will flow. With a single component in the circuit, all of the potential will be applied to moving the current through the lamp. If you place the two probes of a voltmeter on the two sides of the lamp, it will read 9 V.

What does that really mean? The meter measures the amount of voltage that was used

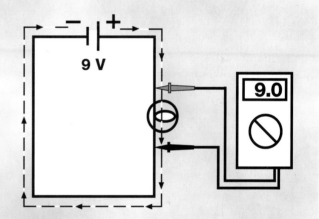

to push current through the lamp. The meter reading is referred to as **voltage drop.** The voltage is reduced, or dropped, 9 V as the current pushes through the lamp. All 9 V of energy is used to push current through the lamp. This is an important idea: The voltmeter measures the voltage drop across a component.

Now put a second lamp in series with the first one. What will the voltage drop be across the original lamp? Will it still be 9 V? Will it be less or more? When you measure the voltage drop across the original lamp with the voltmeter, you will find that it is 4.5 V. Can you guess what the voltage drop will be across the second lamp? It will be 4.5 V as well.

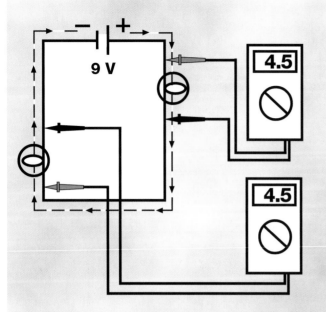

If you placed a third lamp in series with the first two, the voltage drop across each one would be 3 V. Do you see a pattern?

Consider one more problem. If you replaced the two lamps in the schematic above with two 150-Ω resistors, can you guess the voltage drop across each resistor?

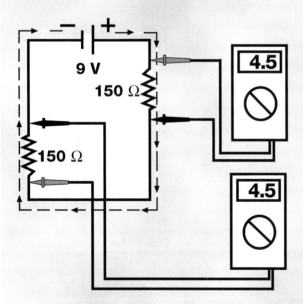

If you put a third 150-Ω resistor in the series, what would the voltage drop across each resistor be? Three volts. And if you had three 1000-Ω resistors in series, what would the voltage drop be across each? Three volts.

THE GREAT TRUTHS

There seems to be a pattern in the voltage-drop results. In 1845 Gustav Kirchhoff, a German physicist, noticed the same thing. He observed that voltage is conserved; no voltage is lost or created when electricity is used to do some work. Based on this great discovery, he generated three statements, known as Kirchhoff's laws, about the voltage and resistance in series circuits. These laws, which we refer to as the great truths, will be useful as we think about working circuits.

The first great truth of circuitry states that **the sum of the voltage drops across the components in a series circuit is equal to the voltage at the source.** Written as an equation, it looks like this.

$$V_s = V_1 + V_2 + \ldots + V_n$$

s = source

n = total number of voltage drops in the circuit

This first truth can be confirmed by reviewing the lamp and resistor circuits discussed earlier. As more and more components are added to a circuit, each one drops a smaller and smaller share of the voltage. But in every case, the sum of the voltage drops adds up to 9 V, the voltage at the source.

These first examples were set up with identical components—identical lamps, all 150-Ω resistors, or all 1000-Ω resistors. What will happen to the voltage drops if resistors of *different values* are put into a series circuit?

Let's look at the circuit with two 150-Ω resistors. If one of the resistors is replaced with a 300-Ω resistor, what happens to the voltage drops? Will the voltage drops across the two resistors still be 4.5 V and 4.5 V? No.

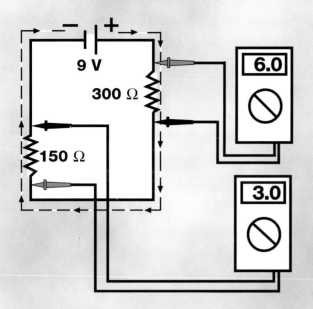

Here's a good way to try out this third truth: How many ohms of resistance does a lamp impose when it is in series with a 150-Ω lamp? We can set up a circuit, measure the voltage drops across the two components, and calculate the percentage of the total voltage available that is dropped by each.

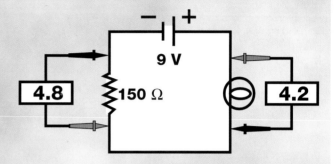

The 300-Ω resistor drops more voltage than the 150-Ω resistor. But the first great truth is still honored. The sum of the voltage drops is equal to the voltage at the source, 9 V. In a similar way, if we set up a circuit with a 100-Ω resistor and an 800-Ω resistor, the voltage drop across the 100-Ω resistor would be 1 V, and 8 V across the 800-Ω resistor.

The second great truth is that **the greater the resistance imposed by a component, the greater the voltage drop across it.**

Then Kirchhoff came to a powerful realization: the voltage drop across a component is proportional to the amount of resistance it imposes in the circuit. In other words, if a resistor contributes half the resistance in a circuit, that component will drop half the voltage. If a component imposes 75% of the resistance, it will drop 75% of the voltage.

The third great truth states that **the percentage of resistance contributed by a component is equal to the percentage of voltage dropped by that component in a series circuit.** This third law is useful for calculating unknown voltage and resistance information about a circuit.

The lamp drops 4.2 V. Set up a fraction and divide to find out what percentage of the voltage is dropped by the lamp.

$$\frac{4.2 \text{ V}}{9.0 \text{ V}} = 0.47 = 47\%$$

The resistor imposes 53% of the voltage drop, so it also imposes 53% of the voltage. Calculate the total resistance.

$$0.53 \times R_t = 150 \text{ Ω}$$

$$R_t = \frac{150 \text{ Ω}}{0.53} = 283 \text{ Ω}$$

R_t = total resistance

Now subtract the resistance imposed by the resistor from the total to obtain the resistance imposed by the lamp. Lamp resistance is 133 Ω, which is 47% of the total resistance.

ELECTRICITY SOURCES AND SAFETY

It was a dark and stormy night. Then, flash...boom, the landscape was illuminated with light as intense as a thousand stadium lights, followed by a shattering explosion. Lightning, the most powerful display of electricity most of us will ever witness, is one source of electricity on Earth. It is estimated that lightning strikes on Earth about 8 million times a day, and a typical strike might be driven by as many as a million volts.

Lightning is the discharge of static electricity. It is similar to the shock zap you get when you reach for the door handle after crossing a carpeted floor, except on a different scale. When static builds up in clouds and the charge is large enough, the charge will flow to ground.

Because of its unpredictable nature, lightning is not useful to humans. In fact, lightning can be a hazard to humans if they have the misfortune of finding themselves where lightning comes to ground. Each year 500 people are struck by lightning in the United States, and Florida is the state that consistently records the most strikes.

Another natural source of electricity is life itself. The celebrated electric eel and a few other aquatic organisms use electric discharge (up to 300 V) as a means of defense. That's extreme.

Most animals, including humans, generate modest electric currents for internal communication. Nerves are electric. Sensory messages travel to the brain, where they are electrically processed, and actions are triggered by electric messages from the brain. Everything from dreaming, to hunger pangs, to the beating of your heart is created, directed, and monitored by electric currents.

The rest of the electricity on Earth is created by humans to do work. Electricity is energy. In creating electricity, some other form of energy must be transformed into electricity. There are essentially three kinds of energy that are transformed into electricity: solar radiation, chemical energy, and kinetic (motion) energy.

Solar energy is the most recent entry into the field of electricity generation. Carefully designed silicon wafers, when exposed to sunlight, convert the energy in light into an electric current. It's just that simple. These silicon wafers are called photovoltaic cells, or simply solar cells. Because of the relatively low power output of each cell, large arrays are needed to deliver a substantial punch. The obvious disadvantage is that they produce electricity during the day only, and not too effectively if there is substantial cloud cover. Still, photovoltaic cells have some advantage in specific locations, such as in remote desert locations and in Earth's orbit.

Chemical energy is converted to electric energy in batteries. The advantages are many, including portability, convenience, and continuous output day and night. They are particularly useful where power demands are low, as in electronic devices. The disadvantages include limited life expectancy and disposal. The spent chemicals in batteries should be considered toxic and must be handled with consideration for the environment.

All other electricity is mechanical. The 120 V of electricity that is universally available in just about every corner of the United States comes from generators. A generator is a big coil of wire rotating in a magnetic field. When the wires pass through the magnetic field, the electrons are pushed in the wires. Electrons in motion equals electric current. It takes kinetic, or motion, energy to turn the wires in the magnetic field, and that kinetic energy can come from lots of sources.

The simplest examples are the wind generator and the hydroelectric generator. In each case a propeller (or turbine) is placed in a flow of fluid. The shaft of the propeller is attached to the generator. When the propeller rotates, so does the generator. The wind generator captures the energy in moving air (put into motion by differential heating of the earth), and the hydroelectric generator captures the energy in water flowing downhill in response to the pull of gravity. Kinetic energy turns into electric energy.

Most other commercial generators burn something or use nuclear reactions to create heat. The heat is used to produce steam, which is used to turn the generator turbine. The primary energy resources are fossil fuels (stored solar energy), such as natural gas and coal, and to a lesser degree wood and domestic waste materials. Nuclear generators use the heat released when atoms are split to heat water. The advantages of these technologies are very high-powered energy, high reliability, and continuous service. The disadvantages are the nonrenewable nature of the fuels burned, the impact of the by-products on the environment, and the potential danger of nuclear disaster.

You may know of other generators, like the portable emergency generators that run on gasoline, or the generator (alternator) that renews the charge on a car battery. These are two more examples of kinetic energy transformed into electricity by...you guessed it, burning something.

SAFETY

You may get the idea from working with 9-V batteries that safety is not a major concern when working with electricity. This is true in only a very limited number of environments, such as this FOSS Electronics Course.

Most of the time safety around electricity is extremely important. Remember the discussion earlier about natural sources of electricity? Our nervous system is an electric system, that operates on very small voltages. If a large current of electricity surges through your body, it can overload and shut down your electric system, including your brain and the system that keeps your heart beating. A substantial jolt of current from an outlet in the wall can make you black out, paralyze your breathing, and stop your heart. This is called electrocution, and it is not a good situation to be in.

What should be done for a victim of

electrocution? First, make sure the victim is no longer in contact with the source of electricity. If it looks like the person is still in contact with the hot wire, don't touch the person. If possible, you should turn off the power source. If the ground or floor is dry, get a stick made of insulating material to move the wire away from the person. A wood or plastic broom or mop handle is good. Then call 911 for emergency assistance.

The deadliest electric encounters happen when electricity passes through a person's body, like from one hand to the other. For this reason, people who work on high-voltage systems have a standard safety procedure of using only one hand to work on potentially dangerous components. If an accident does occur, the electricity might cause burns, numbness, or muscle cramping, but the vital organs will not be affected.

For the electronics hobbyist and the safety-conscious citizen, a few common-sense practices can ensure a safe and comfortable relationship with electricity and electrical appliances. Here are a few guidelines.

- Never put anything but approved appliance plugs into wall receptacles.

- Never use appliances with damaged or worn power cords, particularly if the metal wire is exposed.

- Never use electric appliances when you are in water or standing on wet ground.

- Never place a conductor directly across the terminals of a battery, particularly a large battery like the one in a car.

- Never explore the circuitry of televisions. They can store large charges of electricity for a long time after they have been turned off.

- Be aware that soldering irons are very hot, and avoid breathing the fumes given off during the soldering process.

- Use protective eyewear and gloves when applying force to open an electronic device for study.

Electronic Component ID Guide

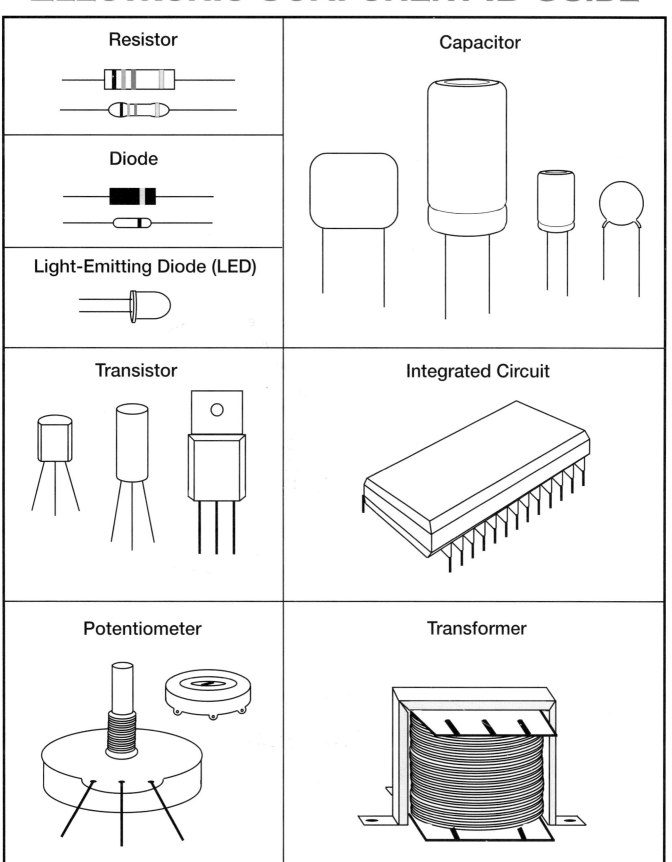

Resistor

Diode

Light-Emitting Diode (LED)

Capacitor

Transistor

Integrated Circuit

Potentiometer

Transformer

USING RESISTORS IN COMBINATIONS

Ms. Waters enjoys designing circuits to provide just the right lighting for the exotic fish in her aquariums. Often she needs to introduce resistance into the circuit in order to get the light intensity just right. Problem is, when she goes to her component cabinet, the exact resistor she needs is often not there. There was a time when this frustrated her, but not any longer. Ms. Waters learned how to use resistors in combination to create a wide variety of resistances.

Resistors can be put in series with one another or in parallel with one another. Ms. Waters quickly discovered how to determine the total resistance imposed by two or more resistors in series—you just add up the values of the individual resistors and that equals the total. Here's one way to think about what is going on in the circuit.

When a current of electricity flows through a wire, it meets with no measurable resistance. The wire is an eight-lane highway through which a lot of charge can flow from A to B. A model for a wire conductor might be represented with a wide line.

A ▬▬▬▬▬▬▬▬▬▬▬ B

When a resistance of some kind, like a 150-Ω carbon resistor, is placed in the circuit, the current is reduced. Fewer charges can pass through the resistor at any one time.

The resistor is like a restriction in the highway between point A and point B, reducing the

traffic flow **throughout the entire length** of the highway. Notice that the current line is reduced to a four-lane highway when the resistor is in the circuit.

Logically, if the 150-Ω resistor is replaced with a 300-Ω resistor, the current highway will again be reduced, to a two-lane road.

And if two 300-Ω resistors are put in series, the total resistance is 600 Ω (total resistance is the sum of the individual resistances), reducing the current line to a one-lane road.

A ─── 300 Ω ─── 300 Ω ─── B

The equation for calculating the total resistance of resistors in series is

$$R_t = R_1 + R_2 + \ldots + R_n.$$

Discovering this equation pleased Ms. Waters. Now she can make lots of resistors, particularly large ones, by using two or more of her resistors in series.

Next she tackled resistors in parallel. The first time she put two 300-Ω resistors in parallel, she was amazed to see that the total resistance they imposed in the circuit was only 150 Ω! How could this be? How could two 300-Ω resistors working together result in less resistance than one resistor working alone? To think it through, she returned to her highway analogy. This is the way she figured it out.

Putting two resistors in parallel is like having two highways running right next to each other. If each 300-Ω resistor is equivalent to a two-lane road, two 300-Ω resistors side-by-side will carry the same traffic as a four-lane highway. And a four-lane highway is the same as a 150-Ω resistor. Two 300-Ω resistors in parallel impose 150-Ω of resistance.

What total resistance would result if a third 300-Ω resistor were put in parallel with the first two? Would it add another two lanes to the highway? The answer is yes, and the resulting resistance is 100 Ω.

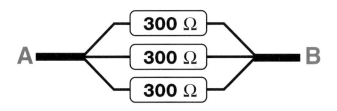

At this point Ms. Waters saw a nice equation for calculating the total resistance imposed by resistors *of the same value* in parallel. She wrote,

$$R_t = \frac{R}{n}.$$

To test her equation, she got out four 1000-Ω resistors and wired them in series. Her calculation predicted a total resistance of 250 Ω.

$$R_t = \frac{R}{n} = \frac{1000\ \Omega}{4} = 250\ \Omega$$

When she measured the total resistance with her ohmmeter, the meter confirmed that her prediction and her equation were right.

Her last challenge was to figure out how to predict the total resistance imposed by two or more resistors in parallel that were not of the same value. She put her 150-Ω resistor in parallel with her 1000-Ω resistor.

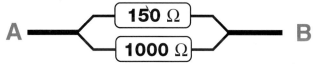

She measured 126 Ω with her ohmmeter. She added the two values together and divided by two, but that didn't work. She was stumped.

Ms. Waters went to her computer and looked up resistance theory on the web. In a few minutes she found the equation she was looking for.

$$\frac{1}{R_t} = \frac{1}{R_1} + \frac{1}{R_2} + \ldots + \frac{1}{R_n}$$

She put the equation to the test by plugging her 150-Ω and 1000-Ω resistors into the equation as R_1 and R_2.

$$\frac{1}{R_t} = \frac{1}{150\ \Omega} + \frac{1}{1000\ \Omega}$$

$$\frac{1}{R_t} = 0.007 + 0.001$$

$$\frac{1}{R_t} = 0.008$$

$$R_t = \frac{1}{0.008} = 125\ \Omega$$

The equation worked. Now Ms. Waters was confident that she could use her selection of resistors in series and/or parallel combinations to create resistors of just about any value she needed.

More single-use cameras than aluminum cans are recycled today. Kodak's the leader, and here's how they did it.

Yanking open an overstuffed file drawer in his office at Kodak headquarters in Rochester, New York, engineer Robert Fischmann pulls out two articles that he has carefully filed away side-by-side: One is a news story from the *Neward Star Ledger,* dated May 15, 1990, describing the Wastemaker Award given to Kodak that year by several environmental groups for excessive and wasteful use of packaging materials in its one-time-use camera. The other is a newswire bulletin, dated December 8, 1998, announcing Kodak as the recipient of the World Environmental Center's 1999 gold medal for corporate environmental achievement.

Fischmann, who heads up worldwide recycling operations for Kodak's one-time-use camera, relishes the contrast between the two. But transforming what was essentially a disposable product into one in which all but one of the components are recovered for reuse or recycling involved much more than a simple product redesign for Kodak engineers.

"Given the choice at the beginning, we would have rather sold a roll of film. However, once we saw that the market for single-use cameras was taking off, we jumped in. But we had a lot to learn about environmental design," recalls Camera Technical Center manager John Spencer, who is responsible for overall product architecture, product roadmaps, and engineering competency for the single-use camera. "The original concept was a throwaway product—after all, we first called it the Kodak Fling—and suddenly we are grappling with questions like, 'How do we design a camera that we can take apart without damaging it and reuse parts of it?'"

Kodak engineers went to work. Since its introduction in 1987, Kodak's single-use camera has gone through four major redesigns, with engineers meeting the same three environmental design goals each time.

- Reduce the material content and energy required in the manufacturing process

- Increase the number of recycled parts

- Increase the number of parts that are reused in new cameras

In fact, the only part in the entire camera today that is not either recycled into new parts or reused is the battery. Kodak gives them away or sends them to steel mills that recover the metal.

CUTTING OUT THE WASTE

Increasingly, engineers everywhere are focusing their efforts on designing green products. A testimony to the successful efforts of engineers at Kodak, the company's newest single-use camera, introduced in 1999, has 75% less material content and consumes 67% less energy in the manufacturing process than the original model (see chart). As a result, Kodak estimates that it has diverted more than 50 million lb. of waste from landfills (based on an average of six cameras per pound). Here's how they did it.

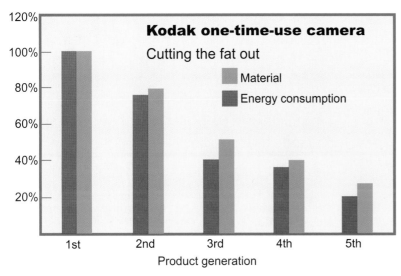

Kodak one-time-use camera

Cutting the fat out

Material
Energy consumption

Product generation

- Switched from a cardboard box to an all-plastic body (itself made of 35% postconsumer resin) and plastic label. "This transition resulted in significantly less card board waste in our recycling operations and at the photofinisher, and created a safer, more efficient film extraction process for lab operators," says Fischmann. The polystyrene-based, pressure-sensitive label is reground and pelletized right along with the cover, which saves both time and waste. Wherever possible, engineers standardized on readily recyclable materials, such as polystyrene and polycarbonate.

- Reduced the wall thickness of many of the molded parts, while at the same time preserving the required structural integrity.

- Incorporated snap features instead of ultrasonic welds to hold together the covers.

- Refined its plastic injection-molding operations.

OLD INTO NEW

The percentage of cameras that are returned and recycled—just over 70% in the U.S.— exceeds recycling rates for both aluminum cans and soft-drink containers. A total of 26 of the 27 (96.3%) parts that make up Kodak's single-use camera are either recycled or reused in a new

camera. That works out to between 76 and 90% of the camera by weight.

In Kodak's reprocessing facility, operators remove the covers, battery, and lens. Many of the parts made of polystyrene, such as the outer covers of the camera, are ground up and extruded into pellets, and remade into new parts. The mechanical and electronic components are inspected and cleaned before being forwarded to a plant where they will be assembled into new cameras. Among the major components that are reused (up to eight times in some cases) are the frame, metering system, and flash circuit board.

But not the battery. "I haven't bought an AA cell in six years," jokes Fischmann, though he isn't exactly kidding around. Every one of the more than 300 million single-use cameras that Kodak has recycled to date that incorporates a flash uses one or two AA or AAA alkaline batteries, and not a single one has gone into a new camera. Although only a small percentage of the battery's energy is actually used up taking flash pictures with a single-use camera (Fischmann's estimate is 10 to 20%), doubts about the exact amount of energy remaining in the battery prevent it from being reused in a new camera. "People don't like to wait for the flash to go off, and the only way to guarantee fast cycle times is to use a brand new battery in each camera," explains Fischmann.

One area of the camera where engineers have improved the robustness of the design is in the high-value electronics system. "Early on, we were seeing things like small cracks and slight leaks in some of the flash tubes. Obviously, they were losing gas pressure out in the field," says Fischmann. "So we started taking a look at some of these failures, and through a small design change have achieved astounding results in terms of quality improvement." Kodak also encourages customers to return cameras that fail, so that engineers can study them and make improvements.

Recently, engineers made a design change to a stamped metal part that synchronizes the flash with the opening of the shutter. Operators were seeing a high number of defects on the camera recycling line, whereby the electric connection was lost or, worse, became intermittent. The original design, which relied on the spring action of a metal part to maintain electric contact at all times, did not always hold up to the banging and jarring cameras encounter during the return process.

To avoid the potential for a flash failure in a new camera, engineers designed a simpler part that is soldered directly to the flash circuit board. "The soldered connection is 100% reliable, even with normal abuse seen in the handling of recycled cameras," says Fischmann. "And it actually costs less than the part it replaced, and eliminated a difficult assembly step."

This kind of continuous improvement in the design of the single-use camera has resulted in excellent yields. "But there's always room to improve," says Fischmann. "For example, if we could just figure out what to do about those batteries."

KODAK'S BATTERY OVERLOAD

Every one of the more than 300 million single-use cameras that Kodak has recycled that incorporates a flash uses one or two AA or AAA alkaline batteries, and not a single one has gone into a new camera. We consulted with battery experts, and asked their opinion on what Kodak can do about its battery problem.

"The issue for Kodak today is that it can't say with confidence how many flashes it can get out of a used battery if it's put into a new camera. So Kodak has created this huge pool of batteries it then has to get rid of," says Francis Clay McMichael, a professor of environmental engineering at Carnegie Mellon University who has been studying the environmental impact of batteries since 1989. "One option for Kodak is smart battery technology, similar to the indicator that you see on some battery packs today that tells you whether or not the battery is good. In fact, there are companies out there today who argue that big users of batteries should have a battery monitoring system in place. The question for Kodak is, 'How costly are these systems and are they good enough today to meet its specs?'"

Kodak insists that any alternative to a disposable battery is cost-prohibitive today. "In a high-volume business like this, a rechargeable battery is not practical from a cost or operational standpoint," says Fischmann. "Besides, if we put too much value in the camera, we run the risk of disrupting our closed-loop recycling. In the meantime, we're looking at ways to make a battery that could be used more than once economically."

Design News 05/15/2000

Article and artwork reprinted with permission from Cahners Publishing.

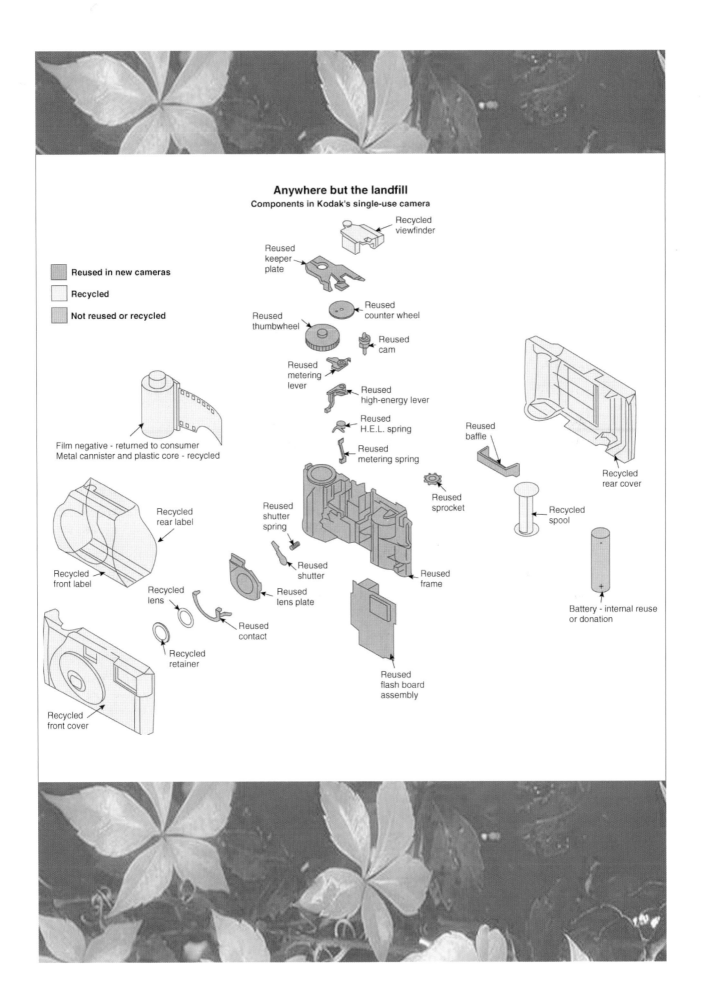

Anywhere but the landfill
Components in Kodak's single-use camera

Reused in new cameras

Recycled

Not reused or recycled

Recycled viewfinder

Reused keeper plate

Reused counter wheel

Reused thumbwheel

Reused cam

Reused metering lever

Reused high-energy lever

Reused H.E.L. spring

Reused baffle

Reused metering spring

Recycled rear cover

Film negative - returned to consumer
Metal cannister and plastic core - recycled

Reused sprocket

Reused shutter spring

Recycled rear label

Recycled spool

Recycled front label

Recycled lens

Reused shutter

Reused frame

Reused lens plate

Battery - internal reuse or donation

Reused contact

Recycled retainer

Recycled front cover

Reused flash board assembly

HOW TO ATTACH A GUARDIAN RESISTOR

Semiconductor components, such as diodes, light-emitting diodes (LEDs), and transistors, are sensitive. They are easily damaged by excessive flows of current, such as that streaming directly from a 9-V battery. In order to safeguard your semiconductors, always include some resistance in your circuits. Not much resistance is required—a 75-Ω resistor will work fine. If you attach a 75-Ω resistor permanently to the negative (black) battery lead, you will automatically put 75 Ω of resistance in your circuits. Follow these steps to attach a guardian resistor to your negative lead.

1. Overlap the black battery lead and the 75-Ω resistor lead as illustrated.

2. Wrap a 6-cm piece of 26-gauge bare copper wire **tightly** around the area where the two bare wires overlap. Make about five turns.

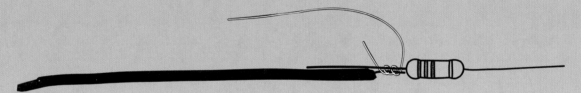

3. Finish by wrapping the rest of the wire **tightly** along the section where the resistor lead and the black plastic insulation overlap.

4. Slide the 7-cm straw over the resistor so only the wire lead of the resistor is exposed.

The Tiny Light with the Big Impact

It really wasn't very long ago that the modern electronics revolution started. It happened at Bell Labs back when your grandparents were school kids. When they went home from school, they tuned in a favorite radio program for entertainment. And great fun it must have been, pulling up a chair or cushion near the big old living-room radio, almost as big as a washing machine, to share in the adventures of their radio pals.

Diode shown enlarged ten times

Radios were big because the components required to pull in the signal, sort it out, and amplify the sound were big. And the vacuum tubes that detected and amplified the signal produced a lot of heat. That changed forever in the early 1940s, when engineers at Bell Labs made a number of breakthroughs in silicon semiconductor technology.

Russell Ohl and Walter Brattain were working on the crystal gizmo that actually detects the radio signal brought to the radio by the antenna. The signal coming through the air comes in a wave. The wave *alternates* between positive and negative, thousands of times a minute.

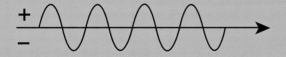

When the antenna intercepts the radio signal, a tiny electric current flows in the antenna. Because of the wave nature of the incoming signal, the current is an *alternating* current, flowing first one way and, a split second later, then the other.

The crystal detector was placed between the antenna and the radio set. The crystal acted like a one-way valve, or, more precisely, a one-way conductor. When the negative part of the signal wave hit the antenna, the current surged one direction, but the detector crystal didn't conduct. Nothing happened. In the next instant, when the positive part of the wave hit the antenna, the current surged in the opposite direction, and the crystal conducted the pulse into the radio. The signal, rather than "sloshing" back and forth, like water in a bathtub, moved in only one direction in little pulses. This made it possible to hear the radio show.

The better detector that Ohl and Brattain developed was made out of pure silicon with just a little bit of contamination. By controlling the amount and kind of contaminant, called doping the silicon, the engineers could get just the kind of action they wanted. They doped one batch of silicon with an element that had electrons to give up (N-type silicon, for negative), doped a second batch of silicon with an element that wanted to accept electrons (P-type silicon, for positive), and stuck them together. The assembled block conducted in one direction. Current would flow from the N silicon to the P silicon, but not the other way around.

There were many advantages to this new semiconductor diode (detector) over the bulky, hot, vacuum-tube diode of the day. The silicon diode was small and cool, opening up a lot of previously unimagined applications. The science of solid-state electronics (as opposed to the vacuum-state electronics of vacuum tubes) was in full swing.

LIGHT-EMITTING DIODES

After the invention of silicon solid-state electronic diodes, researchers set about exploring the potential for creating other solid-state electronic materials. The exploration soon extended to other elements in the vicinity of silicon on the periodic table, both as basic materials and as doping agents. Along the way they discovered that the element gallium, when carefully doped with arsenic, phosphorus, aluminum, and indium, not only produces a functional diode, but one that emits visible light as it conducts! The **light-emitting diode,** or **LED,** was discovered.

Lamps like the traditional screw-in bulb or the bulb in a flashlight, produce light by incandescence. That means that the metal filament gets so hot that it radiates energy in the visible part of the spectrum. A lot of the energy is squandered as heat in incandescent-light production.

LEDs produce light by luminescence, or more specifically, **electroluminescence,** a process of electronic rather than kinetic excitation of material. The excitation squirts out photons of light, and the process is very efficient because only a tiny amount of electric energy is required to produce the light. Electric potential is transformed into light without wasted heat. Pretty good.

Most LEDs are red because the technology for producing an LED that emits red light is cheap and relatively simple. Other colors are possible, however, including orange and green, and most recently the quest for the blue LED has been successful.

USING LEDS

The red lights you see on the front of a stereo set or blinking in kid's sneakers are LEDs. Soon these same LEDs will be controlling traffic in California, thanks to a study conducted by vision scientists at the University of California at Berkeley. They found that not only is a group of the tiny lights as bright as a fixture using incandescent bulbs, but they are cooler and will save the state millions of dollars in energy costs. LEDs last ten times longer than incandescent stoplights. And because they last so long, additional savings will be realized by reducing the thousands of hours that maintenance workers spend changing bulbs.

Caltrans, the California Department of Transportation, decided to move ahead immediately with statewide replacement of its 60,000 red light and pedestrian signals. It has been estimated that Caltrans will save $3 million per year in energy costs with the new red LEDs alone, and perhaps twice that amount if the yellow and green lights are also converted to LEDs.

The tiny lights are grouped in an array of about 300 in one stoplight, taking on the appearance of glistening jewels or an insect eye at close range. At stopping distance, however, the LED array looks like a regular red light.

"We've tested the lights in the laboratory and in the field, and in our judgment there is no difference between the visual effectiveness of LEDs and incandescent bulbs," said Ted Cohn, professor of vision science at UC Berkeley who headed the visual testing.

California was the first state to experiment with the new signals, installing 2300 units in Fresno in 1992. Since then, the cities of Philadelphia and Denver and the state of Oregon have begun using LEDs.

The tests also revealed that LEDs are visually superior to incandescent light when the sun is shining directly into the stoplight. Under those conditions traditional red lights can appear to be on even when they are off. This is much less likely to happen with LEDs.

LEDs grow dimmer, however, in hot weather, losing 1% of their output for every one-half degree above 70 degrees—which could be a problem in hot central California counties.

Caltrans operates about 7% of the signaled intersections throughout the state. (So how many signals are there in California?) Cities and counties, which operate the vast majority of signal lights, are expected to follow Caltrans and install LEDs.

One major advantage of the cool lights, which rely on relatively new semiconductor technology, is that they save lives. Caltrans loses more highway workers per year than does the California Highway Patrol, because its workers are often suspended over an intersection servicing a red light while traffic flows below.

LEDs, the powerful minilights, are strong enough to bring California traffic to a stop!

THINK QUESTIONS

1. Where else have you seen LEDs in use? Make a list and share it with the rest of the class.

2. LED arrays are popular with bicyclists. What are some of the advantages of having LEDs for bicycle taillights?

3. Stargazers use red LED lights for reading their star charts at night. Why do they prefer the red light?

4. What are the advantages and disadvantages of wearing shoes with LEDs built in?

5. Some LEDs produce laser light. What applications do laser LEDs have?

Charge is one of the properties of matter. The two personalities of charge occur at the atomic level. The **protons** in the nucleus of atoms have **positive charge.** The **electrons** that orbit the nucleus have **negative charge.** When an atom has equal numbers of protons and electrons, it is neutral—no net positive or negative charge.

Visualize two neutral atoms meeting. One of the electrons from atom A leaves home and joins the other electrons orbiting atom B.

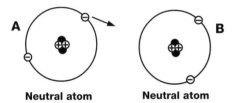

Neutral atom   **Neutral atom**

Now the number of protons in atom A exceeds the number of electrons by one, so atom A has a charge of plus 1. By the same reasoning we can see that atom B now has a charge of minus 1.

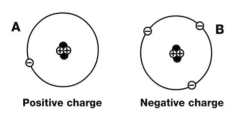

Positive charge   **Negative charge**

The two atoms now have charge because of the movement of the electron. Virtually all electric events are due to the movement of electrons.

Good conductors, like copper, have lots of electrons that are not tightly bound to their nuclei. These free electrons can be made to move from nucleus to nucleus with a little urging. The urging that moves them along in current electricity is voltage.

If a 9-V battery is connected to a conductor, like a copper wire, the voltage will push on the free electrons in the wire.

The voltage will push electrons into the wire until the back pressure, caused by the negative electrons repelling each other, is 9 V. Then the electrons stop moving.

MODERN ELECTRONIC CAPACITORS

A capacitor is a component that behaves a little bit like a rechargeable battery. It can be filled up with charge and used to do a little bit of work. The capacitor works on the principle described—voltage pushing free electrons into a conductive material.

If you dissected a capacitor, you might find a sheet of waxed paper sandwiched between two sheets of aluminum foil, called **plates.** The aluminum foil is the conductive material, and the waxed paper keeps them from touching each other. A wire lead is connected to each foil sheet. The whole package is rolled up like a jelly roll and tucked into a protective outer casing.

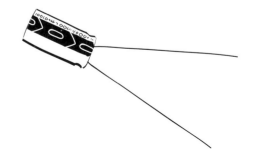

The larger the surface area of the plates, the greater the number of charges (electrons) the capacitor can accommodate.

A source of potential will drive electrons onto the plates of the capacitor until the back pressure (voltage) from the accumulated electrons exactly equals the forward push (voltage) urging them into the capacitor. If you measure the voltage in a capacitor freshly charged up by a 9-V battery, the meter will report 9 V of potential.

Remember when you put the capacitor in series with a lamp, and closed the switch? The lamp flashed very briefly, and then went out. Did you happen to remove the capacitor from the circuit, turn it around, replace it in the circuit, and close the switch? The light flashed briefly again, but this time the flash was twice as bright! Let's see if we can figure out what's going on.

Here's a picture of a capacitor with exaggerated plates in series with a lamp and a battery.

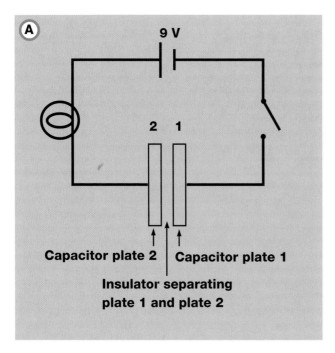

Capacitor plate 2 | **Capacitor plate 1**

**Insulator separating
plate 1 and plate 2**

Because the plates are separated by an insulator, no current can flow *through* the capacitor. There is no continuous conductive pathway. But current *does* flow for a brief moment, somehow, because there is a brief flash of light.

Study illustration A for a minute. Plate 1 of the capacitor is connected to the negative terminal, and plate 2 is connected to the positive terminal (through a lamp).

Notice that the convention of current flowing from positive to negative has been abandoned for now so we can study what *electrons* do in this circuit when the switch is closed.

So why the flash? The battery has potential to push electrons through conductors. The metal capacitor plates represent huge expanses of real estate into which free electrons can be pushed. When the switch is closed, the battery potential pushes on the free electrons in the conductors, driving them into plate 1. But the electrons can't travel across the gap between plate 1 and plate 2, so they accumulate on plate 1.

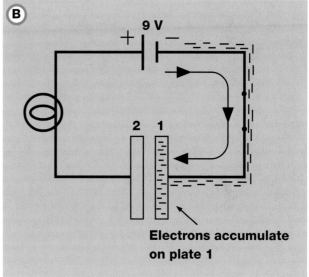

**Electrons accumulate
on plate 1**

As the negative charge builds on plate 1, a negative electric field builds around the plate. The negative field exerts a force of repulsion on negative charges in all directions, including the electrons in plate 2 (the field extends through the space between the two plates). The force of repulsion drives electrons away from capacitor plate 2 with a force equal to the potential across the battery. The repelled electrons flow through the lamp (lighting it briefly) and on toward the positive battery terminal. This constitutes *a brief complete circuit*, as shown on the next page.

27

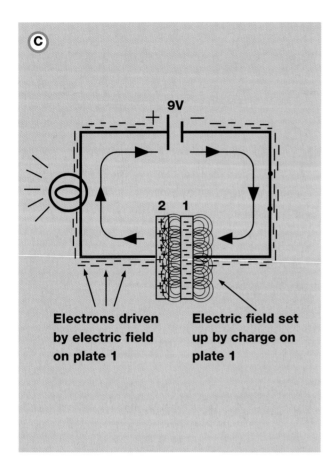

Electrons driven by electric field on plate 1

Electric field set up by charge on plate 1

If you open and close the switch a second time, will the lamp give another brief flash? No flash occurs. A charged capacitor is already "full of charge," so there is no place for electrons to go. Just as surely as you can't pump more gasoline into a full tank, you can't pump more electrons into a fully charged capacitor. The capacitor has 9 V of potential pushing back against the 9 V of potential from the battery.

If the switch is opened at this time, the charge on the capacitor stays put, as shown in illustration E.

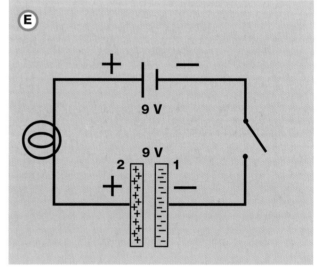

The charged capacitor has a voltage (potential) across it *equal to* the voltage across the terminals of the battery that put the charge on the capacitor. The charged capacitor is rather like a little rechargeable battery, ready to supply a flow of electrons when a conductive pathway connects plate 1 and plate 2.

But why the extra-bright flash of light when the charged capacitor *is reversed?* Because now the circuit has *two* 9-V sources of potential, acting in series. Illustration F shows the charged capacitor reversed, with the switch still open.

When sources act in series, the potential is additive. A 9-V battery in series with a 9-V capacitor will push electrons with a total of 18 V. This creates a very bright flash of light during the brief moment that the capacitor dumps its charge and is once again neutral.

Soon, however, the repulsion between and among the accumulating electrons on plate 1 pushes back against the voltage potential from the battery with a force *equal to* the voltage trying to push electrons around the circuit. When the pushes equalize, no more flow takes place, and the lamp goes out, even though the switch is still closed. This situation is shown in illustration D.

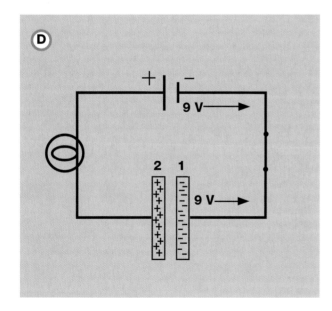

Of course, the continuing potential from the battery recharges the capacitor, with plate 2 now receiving the negative charge (as shown in illustrations B and C), so the light lasts a little longer.

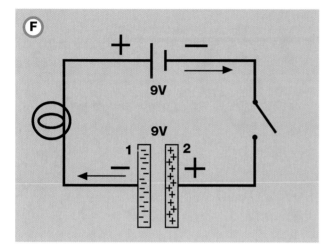

USING THE CHARGE

The capacitor is different than a battery. A battery produces a continuous source of potential using the energy in chemicals. The energy just keeps coming until the chemicals are used up. A capacitor, on the other hand, has the potential created by cramming free electrons into conductor plates. When the extra electrons flow out, the potential is used up, and the capacitor **discharges.**

The quickest way to neutralize a capacitor is to short one lead to the other with a wire. The extra electrons will flow from the negative plate to the positive plate instantly.

The best thing about the capacitor is that it can be used as a little package of charge. Charge it now; use it later. Or charge it here; use it there. Keep this feature in mind as you continue to make more complex circuits. At times it may be useful to have a source of charge—just a little one—to perform a specific task.

Capacitance is measured in farads (F), in honor of Michael Faraday, a great 19th-century electricity pioneer. The farad is a very large unit, so capacitors used in electronic applications are usually measured in microfarads (µF), one-millionth of a farad, or in picofarads (pF), which is a millionth of a microfarad. The capacitors used in this course are 1000 µF, or 1/1000 of a farad.

Capacitors are manufactured in a vast array of sizes and shapes. They may look like tiny pills, colorful buttons, shiny rectangles, tanks, or cans. They always have two leads, but the position of the leads can vary. The leads might protrude from opposite ends of a cylinder, rather like an oversized resistor, or they might both extend from one end, like a silo on stilts.

Some capacitors—those that look like little tanks or silos—are marked with polarity symbols. The 1000-µF electrolytic capacitor used in this course, which has both leads extending from one end, has a negative symbol on the side.

THINK QUESTIONS

1. How are capacitors like batteries and how are they different?

2. Why does a lamp in series with a capacitor flash briefly when placed in a closed circuit?

3. How can you use a capacitor to make a lamp flash extra brightly for a moment? Why does that happen?

CURRENT EVENTS IN CIRCUITS

W e have been talking throughout this course about the flow of current in circuits, but we haven't thought about what it is. Now is the time. Voltage, as we know, is the driving force, resistance is the opposing force, and current is the traffic flow that moves through the circuit.

We can start thinking about electric current by comparing it to water current. Call to mind the mighty flow of the Amazon River. Compare that to the flow of a trickle running down a gutter. These are both examples of currents, but their magnitudes are very different.

The same is true for electric current. The large flows of current pouring out of a car battery when the starter is engaged is an example of a substantial current, while the current in a calculator is tiny in comparison. The bottom line is the number of charges in motion (usually electrons)—the greater the number of charges in motion, the greater the current.

Current is defined as the amount of charge moving past a point in a conductor in a unit of time. The symbol for current is I. Two variables influence the amount of charge in any given conductor: the size of the cross section of the conductor (bigger river), and the density of

charge carriers (free electrons) in the conductive material (unlike water, which has essentially one density). Charge density is very high for conductors like copper, gold, and silver, and low for insulators.

Let's look at current another way. The charge flowing in a circuit is carried by electrons. Electrons flow to produce current. The more electrons passing a "counting station" in a unit of time, the greater the flow of current.

Think of fish as charges. Hundreds of fish are swimming up two different rivers. River 1 is filled with fish from bank to bank, swimming slowly and steadily up the river where they pass through a counting station. At any one time there may be 10–15 fish in the counting window. After 1 minute, 100 fish have passed by the counting station in river 1.

River 2 has far fewer fish, but they are swimming faster. They dart quickly through the counting station one or two at a time. After 1 minute, 100 fish have passed the counting station in river 2 as well.

The number of fish (charges) passing by the counting stations on both rivers in a unit of time is the same. Therefore, the current is the same in both rivers. Notice that current is the number of charges (fish) moving in the rivers, not the water itself.

If for some reason the fish in river 1 got excited and increased their speed, so that 200 fish passed the counting station in 1 minute, the current in river 1 would be twice that of river 2.

If we decide to refer to 100 fish per minute passing the counting station as 1 fin, we can simply say that the current in river 1 is 2 fins, and the current in river 2 is 1 fin. A person hearing this report would know how many fish (charges) were moving up the river at any point in time, but would not know if the fish were moving in large, slow schools or in small, fast groups.

Current is the amount of charge, or the number of electrons, moving past a point in the circuit at a given time. If only a small current is flowing through the circuit, not much work can be done (can't light a bulb or turn a motor), but if a large current is moving through the circuit, lots of work can be done.

Electric current is measured in **amperes**, or simply **amps.** A source of electricity that can move one standard quantity of charge (coulomb) per second past a point is said to deliver 1 amp (A) of current.

Measuring Current

The tool used to measure current is the **ammeter.** Because the amp is a relatively large quantity of charge flow—much more than will be present in a circuit powered by a 9-V battery—the meter is calibrated to read milliamps (mA). By switching the multimeter to the 200-mA setting, the meter is ready to measure current.

As usual, there are rules for using the ammeter. The ammeter *cannot* be connected directly to the battery to see how many amps are available. This will certainly damage the meter. For this reason, the ammeter circuitry is protected by a fast-acting fuse. If you accidentally touch the probes of the ammeter across the two terminals of the battery, the fuse will blow and the meter will go dead until a new fuse is installed.

To use the meter, open the circuit through which current is flowing, and insert the meter probes in series with the other components. The current in the circuit will pass through the ammeter, because the ammeter is part of the circuit.

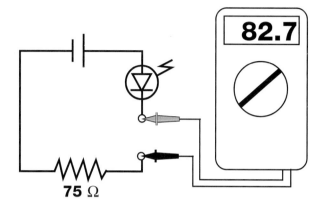

75 Ω

As the current flows through, the meter counts the rate at which charges pass and displays the current. In the example above, the current is 82.7 mA.

If you open the simple series circuit in another location and insert the meter, the exact same value for current will be displayed. Current, unlike voltage, does not drop at each component in a series circuit. The current is flowing uniformly throughout the circuit, never more or less in one place than in another.

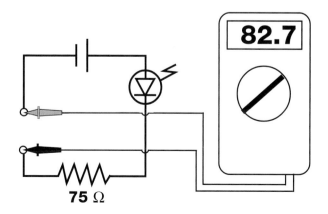

75 Ω

One way to influence the current in a circuit is to change the resistance. If a resistor is inserted into the circuit, the number of traffic diverters (scattering centers) increases. Fewer charges can get through the resistor in a given period of time. The effect of the slowdown in one location on the highway is felt throughout the whole system.

Consider a landslide on a three-lane highway. If the boulders on the roadway restrict the flow of traffic to 30 cars per minute, dodging and skirting the rocks, traffic will back up in the three lanes leading up to the landslide. Beyond the rockfall, where the highway again is unrestricted, the cars will still go by at a rate of 30 per minute, even though they may be going quite fast and be farther apart. At any given point, before the slide, at the slide, and after the slide, 30 cars per minute will pass by. One bottleneck reduces the number of cars moving through the whole highway system.

From this example you can see that there is a relationship between the resistance and the current in a circuit: as the *resistance goes up, the current goes down,* and conversely, as the resistance goes down, the current goes up.

A graph of the relationship suggests that as the resistance gets very large, the amperage approaches zero, and conversely, as the resistance approaches zero, the amperage heads for infinity. This is why you never want to touch the ammeter probes directly to the terminals of a battery. With no resistance, the amperage will head for infinity, burning out the fuse (or worse) in the meter.

The other way to influence the current in a circuit is to change the voltage. Say you have a bunch of 1.5-V flashlight batteries and put them into a circuit one at a time. When you measure the resulting current, you will find that each battery put in series adds 1.5 V to the potential. This results in a stronger push on the electrons with each added battery. The harder the push, the higher the current. Remember the excited fish in the example earlier? Increased voltage excites the electrons, resulting in increased current.

A graph of the data shows a direct relationship between current and voltage.

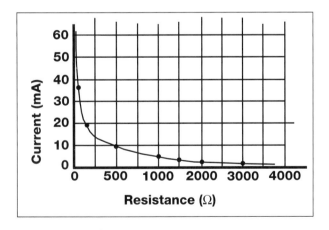

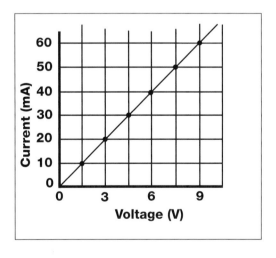

Ohm's Law

The relationship between all three primary attributes of an electric circuit—voltage, current, and resistance—is expressed in an equation called Ohm's law.

$$V = I \times R$$

Voltage drop *(V)* across a component equals the product of the current through the component *(I)* times the resistance of the component *(R)*.

This equation tells us that if we know any two electric attributes of a component, we can use Ohm's law to calculate the third attribute.

For instance, we know that lamps impose resistance in a circuit. We also know that a cold lamp has a very different resistance than a hot lamp operating in a circuit. But it is not possible to measure the resistance of the operating lamp using an ohmmeter. We can, however, measure the voltage drop and current associated with a lamp that is glowing. With Ohm's law, we can *calculate* the lamp's resistance. Here's how.

Set up a circuit with a lamp connected to a battery. Get two meters. Set one to read

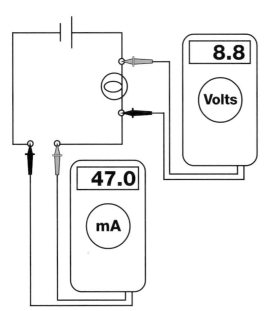

milliamps, open the circuit, and put the meter into the circuit. Set the other meter to measure voltage and put the probes on the two sides of the lamp. The voltage drop across the lamp is 8.8 V and the current through the lamp is 47 mA.

Now employ Ohm's law.

$$V = I \times R$$

$$8.8 \text{ V} = 0.047 \text{ A} \times R$$

(The meter measured milliamps, which must be converted into amps by dividing the meter reading by 1000.)

Now divide both sides by 0.047 to determine the resistance.

$$R = \frac{8.8 \text{ V}}{0.047 \text{ A}} \approx 187 \text{ } \Omega$$

NOTE: The wavy equal sign ($\approx$) is used in equations when products are rounded off. This sign means "about equal to."

If I add a resistor in series with the lamp, reducing its brightness, I can recalculate the lamp's resistance to see if it goes up or down when the lamp glows more dimly. With a 225-Ω resistor in series with the lamp, the voltage drop across the lamp is 3.0 V, and the current in the circuit is 25 mA. Plugging in and solving for *R*, I find that the resistance of the dim lamp is 120 Ω. Great, now I know that cooler (dimmer) lamps impose less resistance.

TRANSISTOR:
An Electronic Landmark

I think I had just entered high school (1957) when I was given a portable radio for my birthday. My family already had a portable radio, but in those days portable meant it was small enough to carry. You still had to plug it in when you got to where you wanted to enjoy the portable music. But this birthday radio was REALLY portable—I could slip it into my shirt pocket, battery and all.

Credit for this giant step downward (in size) goes to the transistor. The transistor, which had been developed at Bell Labs in 1947, was rapidly replacing the much larger and less reliable vacuum tube in the late 1950s. Transistors the size of aspirin tablets were replacing tubes the size of your thumb on up to the size of a small ear of corn. And unlike vacuum tubes, which got extremely hot during operation, transistors were cool. Tiny transistors could be packed close together, making the electronic guts of a radio incredibly small. I felt pretty cool with my radio in my pocket and earphone in my ear, listening to Elvis as I strolled down the street.

Transistors are solid-state semiconductors, made from the same family of materials as diodes. Transistors perform a wide array of different electronic functions. Perhaps their two most important functions are as electronic switches, and amplifiers. Let's see how a transistor does these jobs.

A transistor has three wires coming out of it. We'll call them 1, 2, and 3. If we connect wire 3 to the negative terminal of a battery and wire 2 to the positive terminal (just like connecting a lamp into a circuit), nothing happens. The transistor does not conduct in this situation.

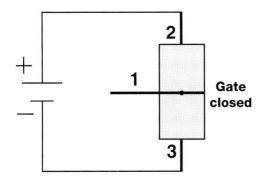

If we connect wire 1 to the battery, electricity *will* flow from wire 2 (positive) to wire 3 (negative) of the battery, and it will flow with a strong current.

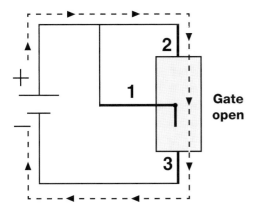

The current will flow through the transistor from wire 2 to 3 as long as there is charge (or current) flowing to wire 1. As soon as the electricity stops going to wire 1, the transistor shuts down, and the current stops flowing through wires 2 and 3.

Wire 1 is like a gatekeeper, opening and closing the gate that lets electricity flow between wires 2 and 3. And the message that tells the gatekeeper when to open and close the gate is electric. That's how the transistor acts as a switch.

An amplifier takes something that is very small and boosts it to a much larger size. In the case of sound, the amplifier takes a tiny, soft sound

signal and makes it big and robust. This is done with an amplifier transistor. Here's how that works.

A cassette tape machine, for example, advances a piece of magnetic tape across a recording head. The tape has an iron-oxide surface, and the recording process creates tiny magnetic patterns in this magnetic medium. Later, when the tape is drawn across the playback head, the little magnetic fields on the tape produce tiny pulses of electricity. These pulses of electricity, called a signal, are exact replicas of the music on the tape, but they are hopelessly puny.

This signal goes to wire 1 of our transistor. Each tiny pulse of electricity that comes into the transistor opens the gate. Each time the gate opens, a huge current of electricity flows between wires 2 and 3. The two signals are exactly the same, except that the output signal is several dozen to several hundred times larger than the input signal. The output is plenty large to operate a speaker, so now we can dance to the music.

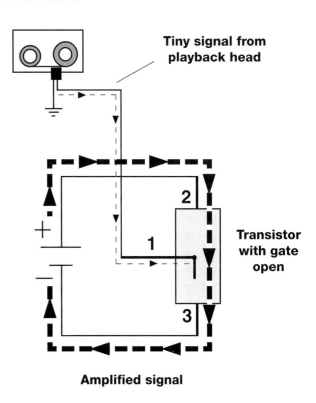

Amplified signal

The invention of the transistor at Bell Labs in 1947 was a monumental accomplishment. The three participating scientists, William Shockley, John Bardeen, and Walter Brattain, were awarded the Nobel Prize in physics (1956) for their achievement. It was not immediately known what the novel devices would be used for commercially, but gradually one industry after another began using them.

AT&T, the huge telephone company, was first to use transistors on a large scale. During the early 1950s, AT&T used transistors in the complicated switching systems required for connecting long-distance phone calls. Before long, the first consumer product using a transistor was developed. It was a new hearing aid that could be carried right in the user's ear. AT&T (Bell Labs' parent company) granted the hearing-aid company the right to use the transistor without paying royalty because of Alexander Graham Bell's lifelong dedication to providing services for the deaf.

The big radio manufacturers were still reluctant to use transistors in their radios, so in 1954 a young semiconductor company called Texas Instruments manufactured the first pocket radio for the consumer market. It had a price tag of $49.95, a hefty price in its day, but the novelty of miniaturization made the radio a huge market success. The manufacturer's challenge was to produce the four transistors needed for the design at a cost of no more than $2.50 each. The same transistor 40 years later cost less than $0.0001. Today for $10.00 Texas Instruments could get 100,000 transistors, enough to build, not one, but more than 25,000 radios.

By the tenth anniversary of the development of the transistor, the market was filling up with solid-state technologies. Transistors were in phonographs, clocks, watches, dictating machines, pagers, automobile fuel-injection systems, toys, and satellites. And the industry was just gaining speed.

The demand for more electronic power in smaller and smaller spaces drove the next innovation in the silicon revolution, the integrated circuit. Through a complicated and exacting process of etching and depositing, multiple transistors could be manufactured on a single wafer of silicon. Called chips, these multiple-transistor components can pack lots of complex circuitry into a tiny space. The early chips, developed at Texas Instruments and Fairchild Industries, had ten or so components on a silicon chip 3 mm square, an area about as large as this printed 0. But that is just where it started. Today a chip about the size of a postage stamp contains more than 20,000,000 transistors! These semiconductor processors are used in computers, where a lot of switching on and off is required.

And where is silicon semiconductor technology going from here? It's anybody's guess. The circuitry keeps getting smaller, and the computing power keeps going up. It has been estimated that a modern pager, if it were manufactured using the vacuum-tube technology of 50 years ago, would be as large as a refrigerator, a cellular phone would require an 18-wheeler to carry it around, and a home computer would be as big as a two-story house. "Home computer" would take on a whole new meaning—you could actually live inside it.

We live in a world dominated by solid-state silicon technologies. Just about everything we do, see, hear, eat, and buy has some connection to a computer or other electronic device. And for now, the transistor is the workhorse that makes it all possible.

Alternating current—An electric current that regularly reverses direction.

Ammeter—An instrument used for measuring electric current in amperes.

Ampere (amp)—A unit of measure for the amount of electric current flowing in a circuit.

Atom—The smallest particle of an element that has the chemical properties of the element. Atoms can exist either alone or in combination with other atoms.

Battery—An energy-storage device composed of electrochemical cells.

Capacitance—The ability to store electric charge.

Capacitor—An electronic component, used to store a charge temporarily, consisting of two conducting surfaces separated by a nonconductor.

Charge—A quantity of electricity.

Charged—Having stored electric power.

Circuit—A conductive path through which an electric current flows.

Circuit board—Conductive pathways printed directly on a plastic sheet to which electronic components are attached.

Closed circuit—A complete circuit that allows electricity to travel from one terminal of a battery to the other.

Component—A device, such as a resistor or transistor, that is part of an electronic circuit.

Conductor—A material capable of transmitting energy, particularly in the forms of heat and electricity.

Conventional current—A positive charge flowing from the positive battery terminal to the negative terminal. Electrical engineers prefer this model, as opposed to electron flow.

Current—The amount of charge moving past a point in a conductor in a unit of time.

Diode—A semiconductor electronic device that uses two electrodes to convert alternating current to direct current.

Direct current—An electric current that flows in only one direction.

Discharge—To lose or release electric charge; to give off electricity suddenly in the form of a spark or arc.

Doping—A process of adding a substance, such as arsenic or antimony, to a semiconductor material in order to change its electric characteristics.

Electricity—A form of energy created by the free or controlled movement of charged particles, such as electrons.

Electrode—Either of the two conductors through which electricity enters or leaves something, such as a battery or a piece of electric equipment.

GLOSSARY

Electroluminescence—The emission of light resulting from a high-frequency electric discharge. Light-emitting diodes produce light by electroluminescence.

Electron—An elementary particle that has a negative electric charge and travels around the nucleus of an atom.

Electron flow—A current starting at the negative battery terminal and flowing to the positive terminal. This model is more accurate scientifically than conventional current.

Electronics—A branch of physics that deals with electronic devices and with the giving off, action, and effects of electrons in vacuums, gases, and semiconductors.

Farad—A unit of electric capacitance; named for Michael Faraday.

Filament—A thin wire that, when an electric current passes through it, acts as the light-producing element of an incandescent bulb or the electron-emitting element in a vacuum tube.

Incandescent—Emitting light after being heated to a high temperature.

Insulator—A material or device that prevents or reduces the transmission of heat, electricity, or sound.

Integrated circuit—An extremely small complex of electronic components contained on a thin chip or wafer of semiconducting material, such as silicon.

Lamp—A device that produces light, either by electricity or burning oil, gas, or wax.

Light-emitting diode (LED)—A semiconductor that emits light when a current passes through it.

Multimeter—An electronic instrument that can measure resistance, current, and voltage.

Negative charge—The type of charge associated with electrons.

Neutral—When the number of protons and electrons is equal; having no net electric charge.

Nucleus (plural: nuclei)—The positively charged central portion of an atom; contains nearly all of the atomic mass.

Ohm (Ω)—The unit used to quantify resistance of current flow in a circuit.

Ohmmeter—An electronic instrument used to measure the amount of resistance in a circuit.

Ohm's law—A statement of the relationship of current (I), voltage (V), and resistance (R) in direct-current electric circuits. The amount of current flowing in a circuit is equal to the applied voltage divided by the circuit resistance; $I = V/R$.

Open circuit—A circuit with a break that prevents electricity from completing the path from one terminal to the other.

Parallel circuit—A circuit where two or more components are connected side by side, and there is more than one path for the current to flow.

GLOSSARY

Photovoltaic cell—An electronic device, consisting of layers of semiconductor materials, that converts light directly into electricity (direct current); also called a solar cell.

Plates—Two sheets of aluminum foil separated by a sheet of waxed paper in a capacitor.

Positive charge—The type of charge that exists on the proton.

Potential—The difference in electric charge between two points in a circuit; expressed in volts.

Potentiometer—A variable resistor with three terminals, often used to control resistance in a circuit.

Proton—An elementary particle located in the atomic nucleus that has a positive electric charge equal to the negative electric charge of an electron.

Rectified current—An alternating current that has been transformed into a one-way, direct current.

Rectifier—An electronic device that converts alternating current to direct current.

Resistance—Force working against the flow of electricity.

Resistor—A component of an electric circuit that resists the flow of electricity and is used to control the flow of electric current.

Scattering centers—Atoms in a conductor that interfere with the flow of electrons.

Schematic diagram—A straight-line drawing showing the layout of an electric circuit; also called a schematic.

Semiconductor—A solid, such as silicon or germanium, that has electric conductivity between that of a conductor and an insulator.

Series circuit—A circuit whose components are connected one after another and that has only one path for the current to flow.

Short circuit—A pathway of low resistance in a circuit that causes the current to bypass the intended component.

Switch—A device that opens and closes the connections in an electric circuit.

Terminal—A conductor attached at the point where electricity enters or leaves a circuit, such as on a battery.

Threshold voltage—The minimum voltage needed to make a diode conduct.

Transformer—A device for changing an alternating current into one of higher or lower voltage.

Transistor—A small low-powered semiconductor device with at least three electrodes; used as an amplifier, rectifier and frequently as part of an integrated circuit chip. Transistors can behave like an electronic switch within the circuit.

GLOSSARY

Vacuum tube—An electron tube that performed the functions now provided by transistors; the basic electronic component in early computers, televisions, and radios.

Volt—A unit of electric potential; 1 volt is the electric potential that will cause 1 ampere of current to flow through 1 ohm of resistance.

Voltage—A measure of energy required to move a charge from one point to another; potential difference between two points.

Voltage drop—A reduction in voltage level caused by a current flowing through a component; the product of the current multiplied by the resistance of a component.

Voltmeter—An instrument that measures in volts the potential difference between two points in a circuit.

Watt—A unit of electric power; calculated by multiplying current by the voltage.

Wire—A strand of metal, usually copper, used to conduct an electric current. Wire conducts electricity with very low resistance.